The Classic Collection
Volume One

Ten Famous Pieces for classical guitar

by

Chaz Hart

A CIP record for this publication is available from the British Library.

ISBN: 1-898466-30-0

© 2000 & 2011 Registry Publications

Audio performances and music typesetting by Chaz Hart. All music arranged and edited by Tony Skinner except where stated. Historical information and performance notes researched by Tony Skinner.

Published in Great Britain by

Registry Mews, 11 to 13 Wilton Road, Bexhill, Sussex, TN40 1HY

Typesetting by

Take Note Publishing Limited, Lingfield, Surrey

Printed in Great Britain

Contents

Introduction

The range of pieces contained within this book demonstrates the breadth of musical styles that can be played on the classical guitar – from arrangements of lute pieces dating back to the 16th century, through some of the standard classical guitar repertoire, and on to comparatively recent Spanish and French impressionist styles. To make all these wonderful compositions as accessible as possible, all the music is shown in both standard notation and tablature (a form of notation that dates back to the time of the original lutenists).

Level of difficulty

In order to demonstrate historical perspective, the pieces are shown in chronological order. The table below shows the level of difficulty of each piece:

Grade 3:

Mistris Winter's Jump – Dowland

Grade 4:

Study in B minor – Sor

Etude in E minor – Tarrega

Grade 5:

Andantino – Carcassi

Romance – Traditional

Soleares – Traditional

Grade 6:

Alman – Johnson

Bourrée – J.S.Bach

Maestoso – Giuliani

Clair de Lune – Debussy

Fingering

The fingerings that have been chosen for this book are those that are most likely to be effective for the widest range of players at this level. However, many alternative fingerings and fingerboard positions could be used and you should feel free to explore any fingerings that produce a good musical result for you.

The following fingering abbreviations are used with the treble clef notation in this book:

1   B followed by a roman numeral indicates the fret at which you should hold down a barre; ½B indicates that only a *partial* barre is required.

2   *pima* are abbreviations for Italian words which refer to right hand fingering (p=thumb, i=index finger, m=middle finger, a= ring finger).

3   Left hand fingering is indicated by the numbers 1, 2, 3 and 4 (with 4 being the little finger). Circled numbers indicate the string to be used.

4   Harmonics are shown with diamond shaped noteheads.

Tablature

In tablature the strings are represented by horizontal lines, with the top line representing the high E string. The numbers on the lines indicate the frets at which notes should be played.

The following fingering abbreviations are used with the tablature in this book:

1   P= pull off.

2   H = hammer on.

3   S = slide.

4   H followed by a number (e.g.H7) indicates play harmonics at that fret.

Performance notes

I've written some text to accompany each piece; the aim being to give you some idea of the historical context and style of each piece. There are also some 'playing tips' to help you cope with the technical challenges of each piece – so have a read through the 'performance notes' before you attempt to play a piece.

Audio recording

All the pieces in this book are performed on the accompanying CD. The purpose of this is so that the listener can quickly and easily get a grasp of the structure and overall sound of each piece. To allow for individual interpretation, most pieces are performed fairly 'straight' – i.e. the performances do not generally feature a large range of rubato or other interpretative techniques. The reader should feel free to add such interpretation where musically appropriate. For the sake of clarity, all recordings were performed using a Rodriguez Model C electro-classical guitar recorded direct input to a Roland VS-880 digital hard disk recorder.

I hope you have an enjoyable journey working through this book. So that you can hear some of my own compositions, I've included a recording of my *Seascape Suite* at the end of the C.D. I hope you enjoy it...

Chaz Hart L.R.A.M

CD running order:

Track	Title & composer
1	**Mistris Winter's Jump** *John Dowland*
2	**Alman** *Robert Johnson*
3	**Bourrée** *J.S.Bach*
4	**Study in B minor** *Fernando Sor*
5	**Maestoso** *Mauro Giuliani*
6	**Andantino** *Matteo Carcassi*
7	**Étude in E minor** *Francisco Tarrega*
8	**Romance** *Traditional arr.Hart*
9	**Clair de Lune** *Claude Debussy*
10	**Soleares** *Traditional arr. Hart*

Bonus Sampler track:

11	**Seascape Suite** *Chaz Hart*

The notation for Seascape Suite is not included in this book. See rear inner cover for details about this music.

Mistris Winter's Jump

This piece was originally written for the lute by the legendary John Dowland – one of history's most respected lutenists and songwriters...

London born John Dowland (1563 to 1626) was the most renowned lutenist of his era; he was a true virtuoso without equal across Europe.

Dowland was also a highly successful songwriter; his *First Booke Of Songes* was a best-seller of its time. Given the continuing influence of his music, Dowland can in many ways be regarded as the pioneer of both English folk music and art-song.

Dowland travelled widely throughout Europe offering his musical services to any Duke or Prince who'd reward him with sufficient gold pieces. He even secured a long term position as lutenist to the King of Denmark, on an enormous salary equivalent to that earned by the highest ministers of state, before returning to England to end his days as a musician to the royal court.

writers' dedication

Dowland, like many other composers of his time, often dedicated music to his benefactors and their family. In this case, Mrs. Winter was an in-law of Lord Vaux. Her two sons, Robert and Thomas, went on to become, with Guy Fawkes, the main conspirators in the famous gunpowder plot to blow up Parliament. So this would be quite an appropriate piece to play by the bonfire next November 5th!

lute arrangement

This arrangement has been transcribed from the lute tablature and the key has been changed to G major to make it fit better on the guitar. It's amazing to hear how many 20th century English folk songs are based on chord sequences similar to this one written by Dowland 400 years ago.

The piece is in the form of a jig, and was intended as a spirited dance tune – hence the title *Jump*. Once you've found your way around the piece it should be played at a lively tempo to capture the feel of the music.

Whilst you should aim to keep on all the bass notes for their full value, the most important thing is to ensure that the melody notes are sounded clearly at all times. If you find this tricky, then omit the middle voice notes until you are comfortable playing the melody and bass together. Just don't forget to add them back in at a later date!

playing tips

1. Experiment using ponticello effects (playing near the bridge end of the guitar) to replicate the treble tone of the lute.

2. Remember, this is a dance piece in style, so omit the rubato that you might use in a standard classical guitar piece from the Romantic era. Instead, try to maintain a fairly even tempo throughout.

3. Notice how bars 5 to 8 are just an elaborate variation on the previous 4 bars. This is typical of Dowland's style of writing for the lute.

4. The melody contains lots of dotted notes. Make sure that you play these with the correct timing as they give the piece its distinctive rhythmic character.

Hear it on the CD – Track 1

Alman

This cleverly crafted piece demonstrates the fine composing abilities of English lutenist Robert Johnson...

At the age of 13, Robert Johnson (1583 to 1633) began a seven year apprenticeship in the *arte of musique* with Sir George Carey. His natural musical talent soon became evident and by the age of 21 he was appointed as one of James 1st's *Musicians of the Lute*.

Johnson rapidly established a reputation as a skilled lutenist and composer. With the accession to the throne of Charles 1st, Johnson retained his post as royal lutenist and was awarded an enviable annual salary of £60 a year – demonstrating the high esteem in which he was held.

dramatic links

Johnson went on to achieve lasting fame as the composer of several instrumental works for the first production of Shakespeare's *The Tempest* – including a little ditty enigmatically entitled *Where The Bee Sucks*. Such was Johnson's reputation that, unlike many lutenists of his era, Johnson's music continued to be printed in collections throughout the century after his death. Today many of his original manuscripts can be viewed in specialist libraries such as the Fitzwilliam in Cambridge. The manuscript for this piece *Alman*, featuring the original lute tablature, can be seen at the British Library – well worth a visit for anyone interested.

dance divisions

Many pieces from the Renaissance and Baroque periods have the title Alman; it simply identifies the style as originating from the old German dance form *Allemande*. Most *Almans* (this one included) follow a similar format: they are of moderate tempo and begin with an upbeat of one short note; there is a highly figured melodic line with a relatively simple accompaniment.

Johnson's *Alman* consists of two eight bar phrases; each of which is immediately followed by a *division*. A division is a form of composition much used by Johnson and other lutenists of the day like John Dowland. It involves creating a variation of the melody by, the simple but effective means of, dividing melody notes into a group of shorter faster notes. Although these were notated for published versions, during performances lutenists would often improvise these divisions as a form of ornamentation. Sometimes tunes would start very simply and build progressively with a series of improvised divisions. During this period, a composer was often judged on his ability to devise divisions on a well-known theme.

playing tips

1. Before you attempt to learn the piece fully, try and play along with the recording just playing the bass notes. This will help you grasp both the harmonic shape and character of the piece.

2. After this, just play the *higher voice* – this melodic line can be isolated by playing only the notes with upward stems in the notation.

3. Once you're thoroughly familiar with both the bass line and the melody it will be much easier to learn the piece as a solo performance.

Hear it on the CD – Track 2

Mistris Winter's Jump

John Dowland
(1563 - 1626)

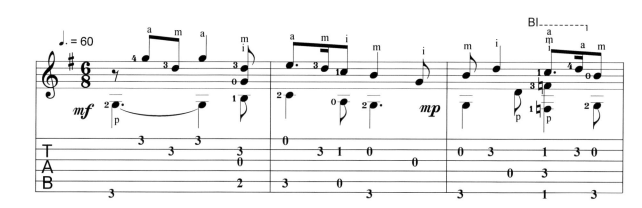

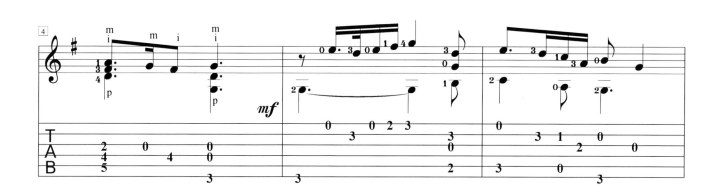

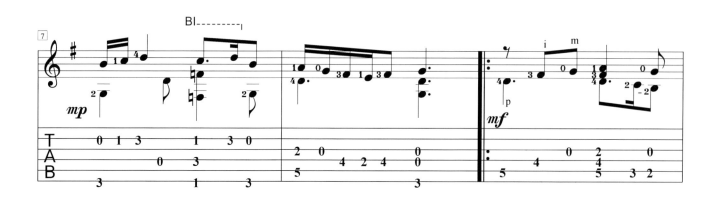

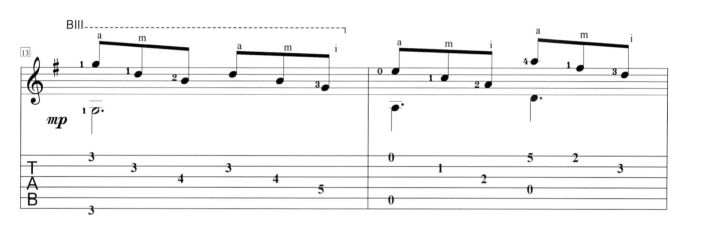

Alman

Robert Johnson
(1583 - 1633)

Bourrée

The world's most highly respected composer of all time, Johann Sebastian Bach, never had the opportunity to write for the classical guitar, but he did write many pieces for its close cousin – the lute...

J.S. Bach was born in Germany in 1685. He came from a long line of musicians and during his lifetime established a reputation as the country's leading organist. He was a prolific composer; writing literally hundreds of works in the baroque style. He somehow also found the time to marry twice and father twenty children – many of whom went on to become successful composers and performers in their own right.

As a composer, Bach never achieved major international recognition until established classical composers such as Mendelssohn rediscovered his writings in the 19th century and brought them to a wider audience.

Today, Bach is widely regarded as the most skilled and talented composer of all time. His compositions include some of the world's most popular choral and religious works (such as the St. Matthew Passion) as well as famous instrumental compositions (such as the Brandenburg Concertos).

counterpoint prowess

The piece I have arranged is a *Bourrée*; taken from Bach's First Lute Suite. It's a great example of Bach's unrivalled skill in naturally flowing *contrapuntal* writing. His skill in the use of counterpoint can be seen throughout this piece as he seamlessly combines two melodies (one in the treble and one in the bass) to produce a unified musical work. Bach is renowned for his skilled writing of flowing bass lines.

A good exercise is to play through just the bass line of this piece before you attempt the whole thing. Amazingly, you'll find that the bass line provides a complete melody of it's own – yet it fits perfectly when combined with higher melody.

dance origins

The title *Bourrée* refers to the name of a dance of French origins. All Bourrées contain certain similar characteristics in that they have: two main pulses to the bar; all main phrases begin on the last crotchet of a bar; and the music is divided into two sections – each of which is repeated.

Whilst you'll need to play the piece at a fairly lively tempo, to capture the spirit of a Bourrée, be careful not to start the piece *too* quickly as the second section contains a lot more fingerboard movement than the first. Choose a speed that you can maintain evenly throughout – even during the hardest bits, like the last four bars.

playing tips

Pieces of this period were often embellished by the performer by adding little effects such as trills and other ornaments to the main music. For the sake of clarity, I've not included any of these in the notation or on the CD, except for the *mordents* in bars 7 and 15. To perform these, play the written note and then quickly hammer-on a note one fret higher and then pull-off to the original note.

Hear it on the CD – Track 3

J.S.Bach – now widely recognised as the greatest composer of all time.

Bach's personality

Bach had a reputation for being very determined in everything he did – some would say obstinate:

1. As a child, when he wasn't allowed access to a large keyboard book he secretly spent six months hand copying the music from it by moonlight every night.

2. He spent so much time studying and sight-reading music that he could play at sight any music that was placed before him. In 1717 he challenged a famous French musician to a public sight-reading duel – but once Bach had played the other musician made his excuses and left.

3. Later the same year, he was arrested and placed in confinement for a month when he tried to leave a Duke's employment; complaining that the expensive new organ the Duke had installed wasn't good enough for him.

4. He was renowned for his abilities to improvise and often showed off by making up complex fugues on the spot.

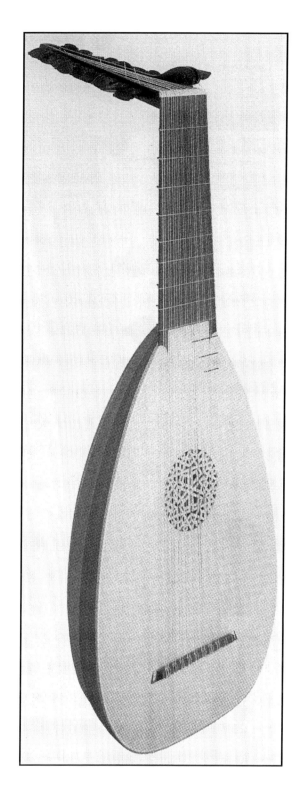

- The *lute* was the precursor of the classical guitar.

- It has a pear shaped body and a round convex ribbed back.

- The lute is strung in pairs – rather like the modern 12 string guitar.

- The lute is still played today and notable players include Nigel North, Julian Bream, and Paul O'Dette.

Bourée

Johann Sebastian Bach
(1685 - 1750)

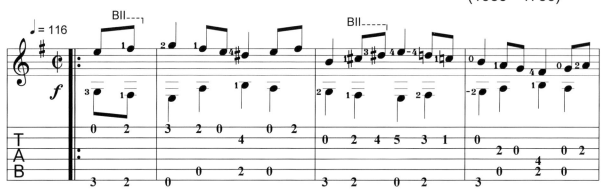

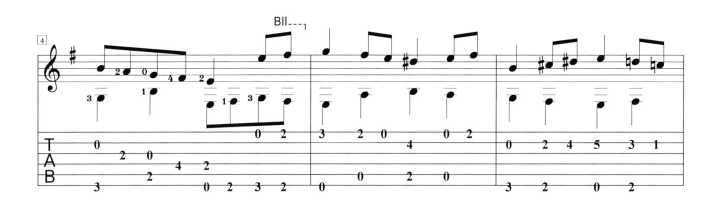

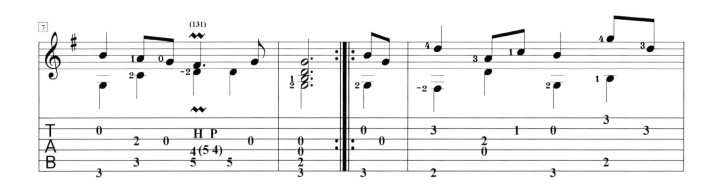

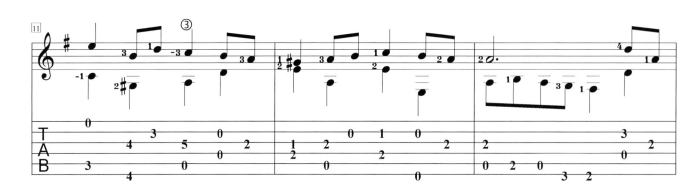

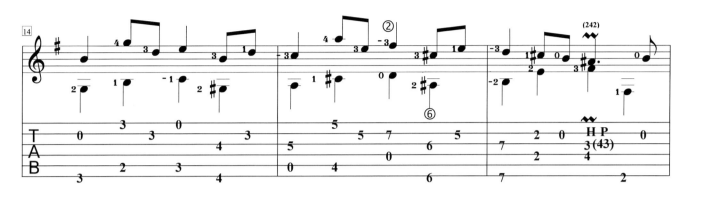

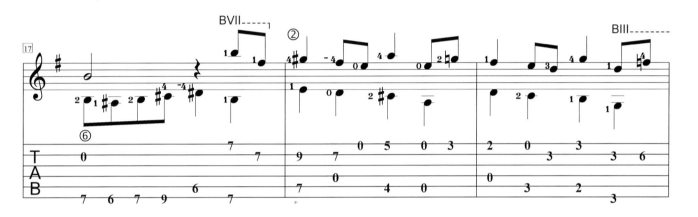

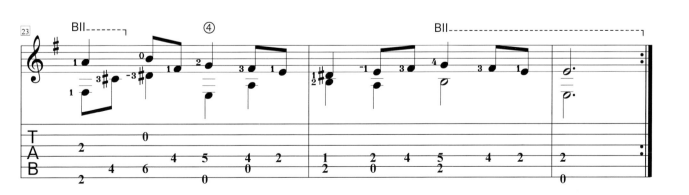

Study in B minor

The much loved 'Study in B minor' by Spanish guitarist and composer Fernando Sor demonstrates why his appeal has never waned...

Fernando Sor is undoubtedly the most influential classical guitarist of all time. 220 years after his birth in Spain, his advanced pieces are still regularly performed and recorded by world renowned guitarists like Julian Bream, Carlos Bonell, David Russell and John Williams.

Anyone learning to play the instrument (no matter at what level or in which country) will always be taught some of Sor's well-written student studies; of which he composed several hundred. Their lasting appeal is due to a combination of Sor's skill as a composer and his complete understanding of the technical challenges of the classical guitar. As Segovia said of Sor's studies "they strike just the right balance between pedagogical purpose and natural musical beauty".

wide ability range

Sor was widely respected as a guitar virtuoso in his day and he travelled widely, living in Spain, Paris, London and Russia. However, Sor's reputation didn't rely solely upon his guitar playing; he was also highly respected as a composer, and he wrote many orchestral works for opera and ballet settings. It was this wide range of musical interests that enhanced his guitar writing. A well-known critic of the day labelled him "the Beethoven of the guitar". Sor's *Methode pour la guitar* remains one of the most comprehensive and insightful guitar teaching books ever written.

effective study

Sor's well-known *B minor study* has remained a favourite with guitar players for many years due to its simple, but highly effective musical structure. Yet it was designed specifically to enable students to work on the technical challenge of extracting a melody from an arpegiated accompaniment consisting of just a series of chords.

If you look at the notation, you'll notice that certain notes have upward stems. This indicates that these are the melody notes; the other notes act only as an accompaniment. When played together they should almost give the listener the impression of hearing two guitars. To achieve this, make sure that the accompaniment part never overpowers the melody.

playing tips

There are many ways of interpreting this piece and of getting the contrast in volume and tone between the two voices.

1. The most obvious method is to use a rest stroke for the melody notes, so that your picking finger is held straight and comes to rest on the adjacent lower string. This will result in a strong but rather brash tone.

2. My preferred method is to use *free* strokes throughout, and to angle the third finger anti-clockwise so as to extract extra volume from the melody notes without making them sound too forced.

3. Either of the two methods outlined above will suffice – the important thing is to ensure that the accompaniment is not too loud.

Hear it on the CD – Track 4

Maestoso

Italian virtuoso Mauro Giuliani uses this piece to demonstrate the effective use of octave playing technique on the classical guitar...

Born in 1781, Mauro Giuliani was a naturally talented multi instrumentalist. By his late teens he had already gained a nation-wide reputation as a guitar virtuoso in his native Italy. By the turn of the century a hugely successful European concert tour established him as the most accomplished guitarist of the period.

Giuliani performed with many of the top musicians of the day and Beethoven proclaimed him as making the guitar sound like "a miniature orchestra". He settled in Austria and developed a rewarding career as a performer and teacher to the Austrian aristocracy.

Giuliani became a prolific composer; over 300 of his works were published, ranging from student studies to full blown guitar concertos. The world's first ever guitar magazine published in 1833 was titled 'The Giulianiad' in his honour, exclaiming in the first issue that "in Giuliani's hands the guitar became gifted with a power of expression at once pure, thrilling, and exquisite".

Giuliani's music has always maintained its popularity and is still widely played today both by students and recitalists.

guitar techniques

This piece is from Giuliani's collection of 24 musical exercises – Opus 48. Whilst it is complete as a piece of music in its own right, it is also designed to introduce the player to certain technical challenges:

1. In the first eight bars the melody notes are indicated by the use of *tenuto* lines; these notes should be held and slightly emphasised. Take great care not to play the repeated open G string notes too strongly – these are intended just as *pedal notes* and are there mainly to provide a sense of movement to the music, rather than have any important melodic function.

2. Bars 9 to 14 feature a fine array of fast octave runs across the fingerboard. As fret widths get progressively smaller towards the *dusty* end of the fingerboard, you'll need to practise varying the left hand span accordingly to avoid fretbuzz when changing fingerboard position.

3. Bars 15 to 16 feature a really flashy sounding arpeggio run. In fact, this purely consists of picking through a sequence of simple G major chord shapes. If you practise the chord shapes first you'll find it much easier to play up to speed when you add the picking. A similar sequence occurs in bars 19 to 20 – but based on C major chords.

playing tips

Although the whole piece is written in semiquavers and suggests a fair turn of speed, the secret to success with this piece is to learn it very slowly making sure that you achieve a high degree of clarity and articulation.

This 'slow and careful' learning approach will provide a firm foundation for when you come to play the piece at performance tempo.

Hear it on the CD – Track 5

Study in B Minor

Fernando Sor (1778 -1839)

Maestoso Op.48 No.13

Mauro Giuliani
(1781 - 1829)

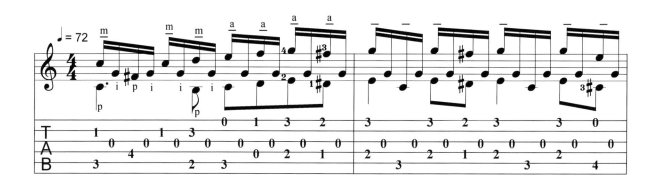

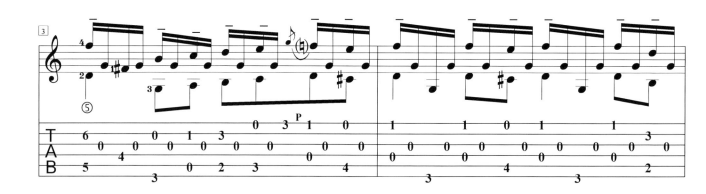

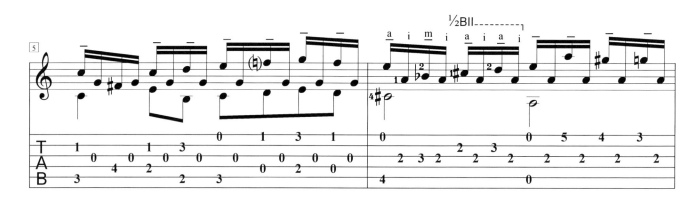

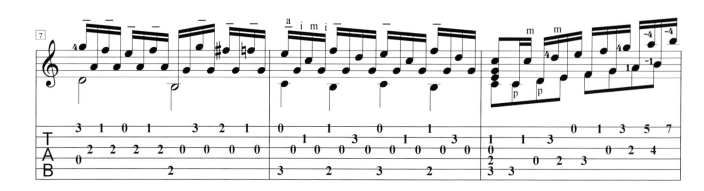

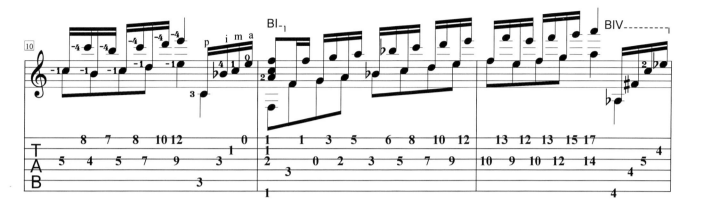

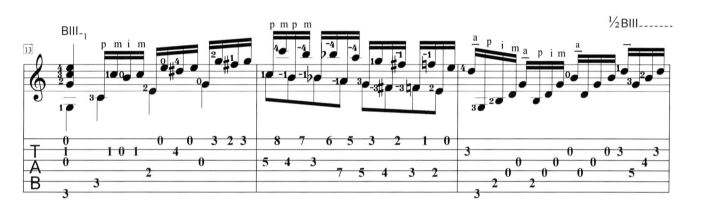

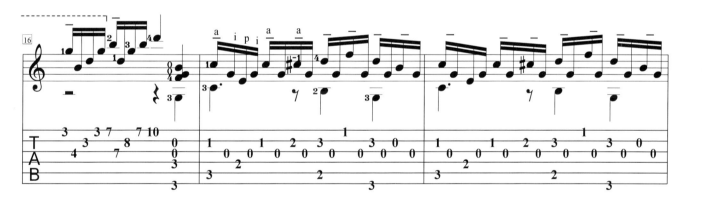

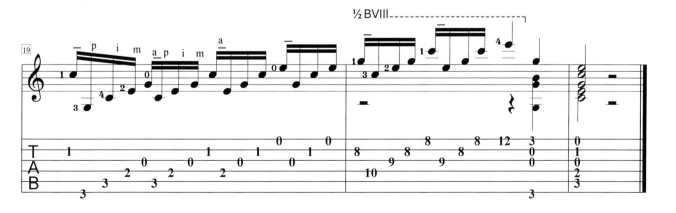

Andantino

Written nearly 150 years ago, this Carcassi study is still one of the most popular pieces in the classical guitar repertoire today...

The Italian guitarist and composer Matteo Carcassi (1792-1853) was one of the greatest guitar players of his era. Born in Florence, he undertook regular concert tours throughout Europe and established himself in Paris as guitar teacher to the rich and famous. He published a tuition method which became the best selling guitar study book of the 19th century.

Carcassi wrote literally hundreds of pieces for guitar, including many instructive studies. This piece is No.3 from his most popular collection *25 Progressive Melodic Studies Opus 60* and is commonly known as *Study in A*. The lasting success of this collection reflects the fact that Carcassi's studies were not just technical exercises – but were always effective pieces of music in their own right.

chordal study

This study is chordal based and it's important to build, and then hold down, the chord shapes within each bar to achieve a smooth legato (over-ringing) sound. Each bar consists of just one chord – plus a small variation; for example, bar one is A6 to A major. Learning the chord shapes first will cut down the time required to learn the piece and will give you a greater understanding of the structure of the piece.

musical balance

Look closely at the music and you'll notice that some notes (normally those that fall on the second and third crotchet beats) have stems that go in both directions. This indicates a melodic emphasis within the music; whilst these notes should be played slightly louder and allowed to ring for their full value, there is no need to over accent them with a heavy rest stroke. Experiment by varying the balance between the *melody* notes and the accompaniment.

using rubato

To make the performance more like a piece of romantic music and less like a technical study, it's essential to use both rubato and dynamic variety within phrases. Allow both the tempo and volume to subtlety rise and fall throughout the piece. Don't try and copy the recording in this respect, instead try and develop your own feel for how the music is written so that it naturally rises and falls in certain places.

playing tips

1. The right hand picking pattern for this piece stays the same all the way through – except in bar 16 and a variation in the last couple of bars of each section. So it's worth practising this (pim,aim,aim,pim) pattern on just a simple chord until you feel really relaxed with it.

2. The second half of bar 16 uses straight quavers rather than triplets. Listen to the recording to hear this change of timing.

3. Bar 17 onwards is very similar to the beginning of the piece, but notice that this time all the bass notes are A notes – this effect is called a *pedal point*; it can be used to create tension and dramatic impetus in a piece.

Hear it on the CD – Track 6

Étude in E minor

A typically beautiful piece by Francisco Tárrega – the man generally hailed as 'the father of modern classical guitar technique'...

Francisco Tárrega (1852-1909) laid much of the groundwork for the popularity of the guitar in the twentieth century; his talent and dedication resulted in a significant extension of the guitar's technique and repertoire. The title of this piece, *Étude*, simply means a musical *study*. Tarrega wrote a whole series of these, but they were never merely technical exercises – he always ensured that each study was a worthwhile piece of music.

highlight the tune

Tárrega's aim in this study was to demonstrate how a melody could be extracted from within a piece that, at first, appears to consist of just arpeggio picking on chords. If you play only the notes on the first string you will discover a haunting and wistful melody. Whilst the simple right hand picking pattern stays the same throughout the piece, the first string notes should be slightly emphasised and allowed to ring. This can be done by using a *rest stroke*; by picking the first string firmly and then coming to rest on the second string, this action will accent the melody notes with a strong tone.

playing tips

1. The chord at the end of bar 12 calls for a wide stretch. Try not to take the bass note off, instead allow your left hand thumb to move at the back of the neck.

2. The H12 sign in the final bar means play the notes as harmonics at the 12th fret.

3. To capture the romantic spirit of the piece feel free to use some *rubato* (subtle tempo changes especially at the end or beginning of phrases) particularly in the repeat section. A bit of vibrato (wavering the pitch of the note by rocking the fretting finger horizontally) will help to embellish the melody. Finally, don't forget to follow the dynamic markings; these gradual changes in volume can really help to emphasise melodic shaping and phrasing in the tune.

Hear it on the CD – Track 7
---

10 things you never knew about Tárrega

1. He started out working in a Spanish rope factory.

2. He had impaired vision and both his piano and guitar teachers were blind.

3. He couldn't choose between pursuing the guitar or piano – so he gave a concert performing on both and asked the audience to decide for him.

4. His playing career began as a street and cafe musician, even sometimes playing for bandits in the Spanish mountains.

5. He set himself a rigorous daily practice regime, including improvising before breakfast, scales and arpeggios all morning, and composing and transcribing all afternoon.

6. He loved cigarrillos and sometimes he'd resort to playing phrases with just his left hand so that he could smoke while he performed.

7. He insisted on musical accuracy and split up with his lover and duet partner after she simplified a difficult guitar fingering saying "I'd have preferred a knife stabbed in my heart than a note taken from my music".

8. As well as composing many original works (including the popular tremolo study *'Recuerdos de la Alhambra'*) he made hundreds of guitar arrangements of piano pieces by Beethoven, Albeniz, Chopin and other masters.

9. He disliked the sound of strings plucked by fingernails, considering the sound too harsh, and instead played off the flesh in order to achieve a warmer tone.

10. Several of his pupils, such as Pujol and Llobet, went on to become renowned guitarists and composers.

Andantino Op.60 No.3

Matteo Carcassi
(1792 - 1853)

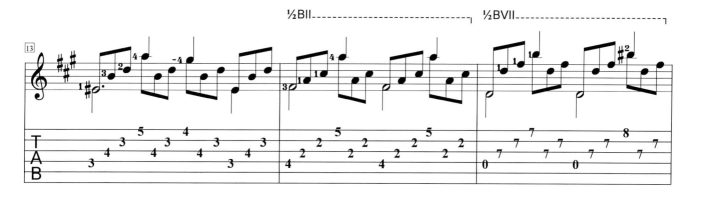

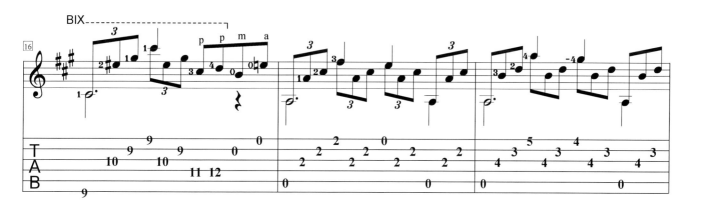

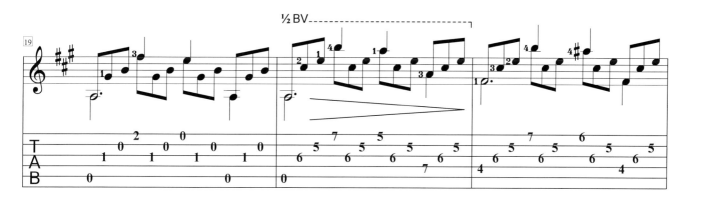

Étude in E Minor

Francisco Tárrega
(1852 - 1909)

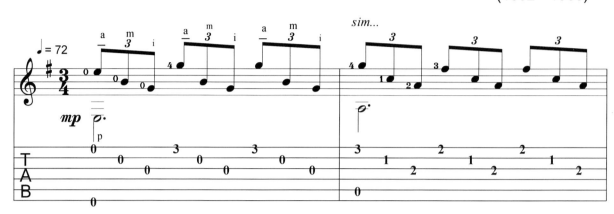

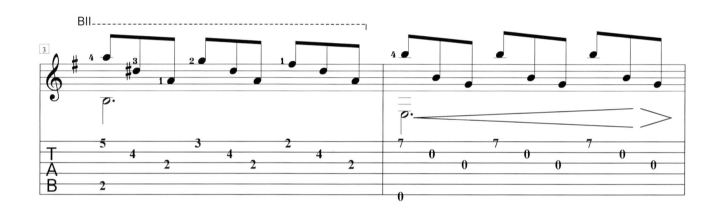

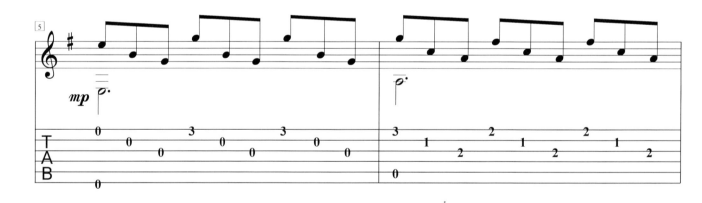

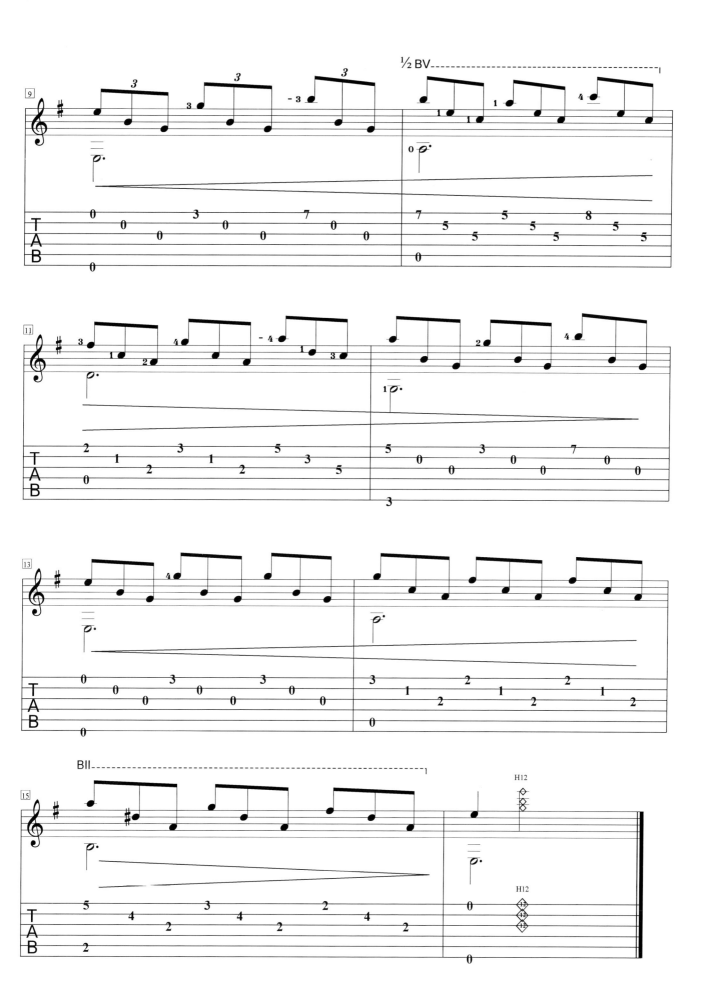

Romance

Although no one knows exactly where this piece comes from, it remains one of the most popular guitar melodies ever written...

The exact origins of this traditional Spanish melody are somewhat of a mystery, but one thing is for sure – throughout the past 100 years or more it has remained the most popular piece of music for the classical guitar.

chords and melody

The right hand picking pattern for this piece stays exactly the same the whole the way through – therefore it's a good idea to practise just this pattern on the open strings until you can almost play it in your sleep.

The piece consists of a melody with an arpeggiated chordal accompaniment. If you look closely at the music you'll notice that some notes (normally the first of every triplet) have stems that go in both directions. This is to indicate where the melody lies. These melody notes should be played quite strongly, so that they sound clearly above the accompaniment. Using a *rest stroke* to play these first string melody notes is one solution; alternatively you can strike the right balance by simply reducing the volume at which you play the accompanying second and third strings. Play through the first string notes on

their own at first – that way you'll have a clear idea of what the melody should sound like.

Careful use of vibrato in places can give a sonorous tone which will help to emphasise the wistful nature of the melody. Keep the fretting finger in contact with the string whilst rocking the hand from side to side horizontally to achieve a vibrato effect.

playing tips

1. At bar 17 the piece changes from the key of E minor to E major. You can bring out the brighter mood of the major key by shifting the picking hand farther towards the bridge for this section.

2. Notice how in bars 19 & 20 the melodic line switches to the second string for the only time during the entire piece.

3. Bar 27 contains the most difficult stretch of the whole piece. Be careful not to overstrain the hand when trying this at first – take a deep breath just before this point and then try and let the hand muscles relax.

Hear it on the CD – Track 8

Clair de Lune

Debussy's much loved impressionist piano piece is well suited to the tonal nuances of the classical guitar...

French composer, Claude Debussy (1862-1918) began piano lessons at a very early age. His progress was so remarkable that he entered the Paris Conservatory at the age of 11. He remained there for 10 years – alternately winning prizes and perplexing his teachers with his revolutionary musical ideas. He was a rebellious student – impatient with the prevailing academic theories saying "there is no musical theory – you merely have to listen and fantasise". Paris of the late 19th century was a melting pot of cultural diversity and artistic influence and the young Debussy fell in with Symbolist poets, like Baudelaire and Mallarme, whose credo was that art should appeal to the senses before the intellect, and should subtlety suggest meaning rather than state it. Consequently, much of Debussy's music has a dreamy quality – which resembles the pictorial effect achieved by Impressionist painters of the day like Monet. His music made its impact by creating moods and impressions; emphasising simplicity and space. The music of Debussy had a monumental impact on Western music in that he liberated it from the limitations of traditional harmony, and the high quality of his output proved to later composers the worth of experimenting with new ideas and techniques.

expressive piano

From 1902 to 1910 Debussy wrote chiefly for the piano, rejecting the traditional percussive approach to the instrument and emphasising instead its capabilities for delicate expressiveness. *Clair de Lune* is arranged from the piano *Suite Bergamasque* – composed in 1890 and published in 1905. A reviewer of the time wrote "Debussy cradled the piano, talked softly to it, like a rider to his horse". This gives you an idea of the subtle approach you should take when performing the piece.

Playing tips

To capture the spirit of Debussy try and incorporate some of the following effects:

Rubato: this means to 'rob time' – experiment by slowing down in places and then speeding up again to make up lost time.

Dynamics: vary the volume to create a dramatic effect – playing some phrases very softly can draw the listener into the music.

Glissando: sliding from one note to another smoothly – a good example is at the end of bar 8.

Rallentando: slowing down at the end of a phrase – this can help you to shape the melody in an individual way.

Hear it on the CD – Track 9

Romance

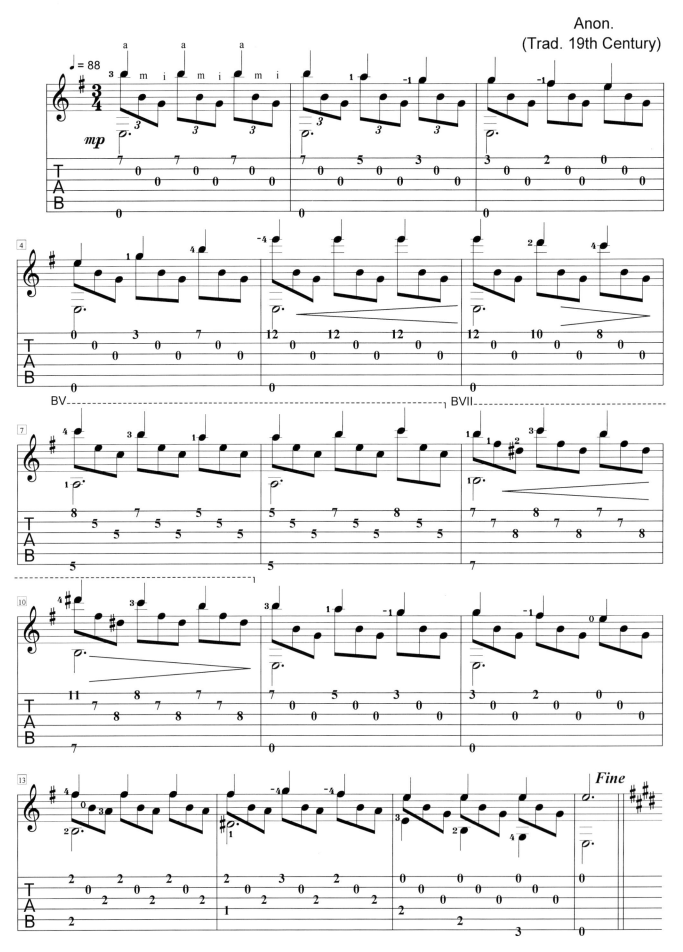

Clair de Lune

Claude Debussy (1862 -1918)

Soleares

Arranged by Chaz Hart

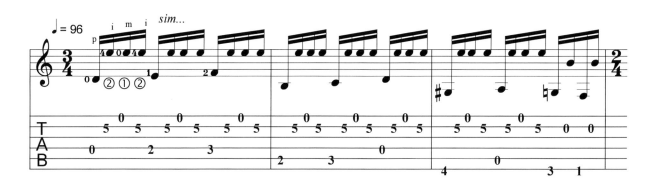

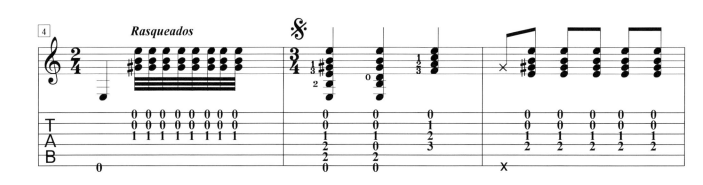

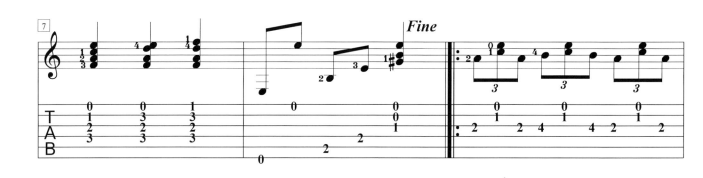

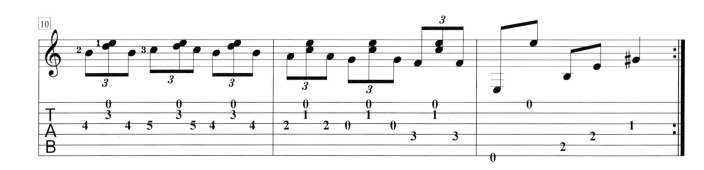

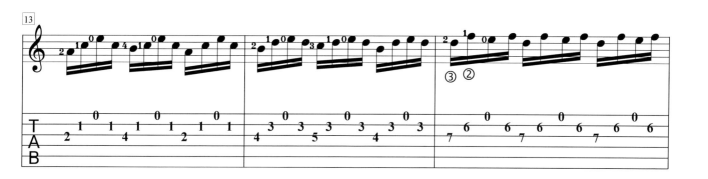

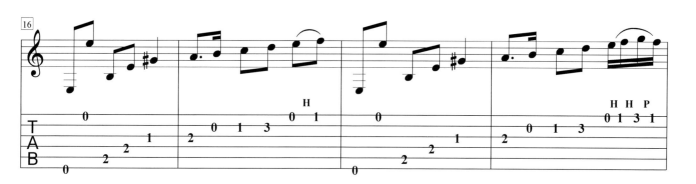

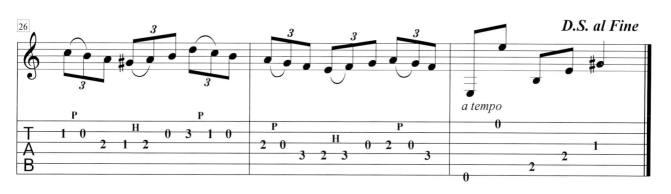

Soleares

The combination of Moorish and Spanish music resulted in the unique passionate sound of flamenco...

The invasion of southern Spain in the 15th century by the Moors from North Africa created a very distinctive and exotic influence on the music of Spain. This resulted in southern Spanish music developing a unique character. The typical flamenco guitar style that we know today has been largely developed from this tradition.

What is Flamenco?

The term Flamenco stems from a Spanish word meaning to flame, i.e. to dazzle and impress. Traditionally the guitar plays a supporting role to the singers and dancers; who are considered to be the main features of any flamenco show. It is only relatively recently that flamenco guitar has come to be performed and recorded as a solo instrument. But whether played solo or in an accompaniment role, all flamenco guitar is based on a range of traditional dance rhythms such as *Alegrias, Bulerias, Sevillanas* and *Soleares*. Each has its own unique *compas* (underlying rhythm) that sets the mood and feel of the music.

flamenco rhythms

The Soleares that I have arranged and recorded is a *Soleares por Arriba* – indicating that, although it is based in the key of A minor, the dominant chord of E major provides an important harmonic role. This gives the Soleares style a certain strength of sound that contrasts with and complements the mellowness of the minor key. Although notated in $\frac{3}{4}$ time for ease of reading, the compas of Soleares can be counted in 12 beat sections – accenting beats 3,6,8,10 and 12. These beats do not have to be accented

by the guitarist – they simply indicate the shape of the melodic line and underlying rhythm that is sometimes clapped by the singers.

I have notated only the first half of the piece as it appears on the CD, as after this I have created an improvisation based on the same theme (this is known in flamenco as a falseta). Notice that whilst I have used the A natural minor scale as a basis for the improvisation (consisting of the notes A,B,C,D,E,F and G) I occasionally alter it to include a G# (sharp) note taken from the E major chord (this gives the same effect as using A harmonic minor scale). Once you've found your way around the main piece, try and invent your own falseta.

playing tips

1. In bars 1 to 3 allow the fretted E notes to over-ring against the open E string to create a tremolo effect.

2. Bar 4 contains *rasqueados* – this is a classic flamenco strumming technique. Strum the strings by releasing the first three fingers in quick succession – so that the fingers rapidly roll across the strings one after another.

3. Bar 6 features a *golpe*. This is a percussive effect achieved by striking the body of the guitar with the ring finger. Feel free to add in more golpes from time to time if you get the urge! If using a classical guitar be careful not to damage the finish – flamenco guitars are fitted with perspex golpe plates to avoid this problem.

Hear it on the CD – Track 10